Dear Parents

As we all know, from an early age, the information our children learn about religion will later influence their beliefs, attitudes, and behaviors in later years.
This series tells about the birth, infancy, and childhood of Prophet Muhammad (peace and blessings be upon him), with stories and drawings that will appeal to our children and help them to understand.
We hope and believe that you and your children will enjoy this series and find the stories not only entertaining, but informative as well.

2

THE SHELTERING CLOUD

The white clouds had gone out on a midnight excursion. They looked like cotton candy strung across the night sky. As they floated through the sky, thcy talked among themselves. The moon, who provided light for them, joined in their pleasant conversation.

A cloud that looked like an umbrella started the conversation: "I am so excited, and you'll never guess why!"

The smallest cloud said: "Oh, don't tease…tell us what has made you so excited."

The umbrella-shaped cloud answered: "Tomorrow I head toward Mecca. There is a caravan preparing to go to Damascus. Among them is a wonderful child whom Allah loves very much. Allah has given me the job of sheltering him from the burning sun."

"I will go and provide shade for him. I will be like an umbrella for him."
While the cloud was talking the little cloud nearly burst with curiosity.
"Tell us more, Umbrella Cloud, tell us more! Who is this wonderful child?"
The umbrella-shaped cloud looked fondly on the little cloud, and went on with his tale. "He is like the most valuable pearl of this world; his name is Muhammad. He will tell people that Allah has created everything and that He is the only Creator. As the clouds continued to talk, the time for the Sun to rise approached. The umbrella-shaped cloud said goodbye to his friends and the Moon, and headed off to Mecca.
He soon reached the caravan, which had already left for Damascus.

The umbrella-shaped cloud flew merrily on the way, happy with the task that had been given to him. All along the journey, he thought how fortunate he was to be able to protect Muhammad, the Child of Light. At this time the caravan set up camp in a town near Damascus where its members found food and rest.

8

The Child of Light shone out like the Moon from the middle of the crowd. Seeing this beautiful boy, the cloud felt so excited that he wanted to shout with joy.

"What beauty Allah has created, what a beautiful child," the cloud thought to himself. He was so overcome that he had to work hard to stop rain drops from falling … He wanted to embrace the child, but his job was to shelter him.

Just at that moment a bird flew by the cloud. The cloud wanted to share his joy with someone else. He called out to the bird: "Can you see, my friend, can you see him too?" The bird understood. She had flown from a tree that was near where the child was staying. She was also very excited to have seen the Child of Light: "I see him, my friend. Do you know, I love the Child of Light as much as you do!" the bird answered.

The two friends were able to share their love for the Child of Light. The bird said: "Did you know my friend, in the place where the caravan is staying, there is a priest called Bahira? He is a very wise man. From him, I learned of a holy book that talks about the last prophet who will be sent to human beings. This book also describes the last prophet. Let's go and see what Bahira will do when he sees the Child of Light."

The umbrella-shaped cloud said: "He will be very surprised when he sees that I settle over the child's head and that I will never leave."

Just then, pointing in the distance, the bird said:

"Look, do you see, my friend, here comes Bahira. He is looking up at you and then again at the Child of Light. He can't take his eyes off the child. He looks very thoughtful. I think he understands everything."
The cloud said:
"Now he is going up to the uncle of the child, Abu Talib." Bahira approached Abu Talib and said: "This child is a very special and important person. He carries the characteristics of the final prophet described in our holy book. Please take good care of him."

15

Upon hearing this, Abu Talib cut his journey short and took his beloved nephew, Muhammad (peace and blessings be upon him), back to Mecca.

The yellow bird chirped as she looked with all the love in her heart at the Child of Light. On this unforgettable day, she bid farewell to her friend the umbrella-shaped cloud. All through the journey, the cloud did not leave his post above the head of the child.

He flew with happiness through the sky, thrilled at the task that had been entrusted to him.